Richard Rodney Benne

Sonatina

for clarinet solo

TGW7C 3rd mvt

Commissioned by the Mid-Northumberland Arts Group for the National Clarinet Competition for Young People 1983.

I   Con fuoco
II   Night thoughts (Lento)
III   Scherzando

DURATION ABOUT 7 MINUTES

Order No: NOV 120549
NOVELLO PUBLISHING LIMITED
8/9 Frith Street, London W1V 5TZ

To Angela Morley

SONATINA
for clarinet solo

RICHARD RODNEY BENNETT
1981

CLARINET IN Bb

1

Con fuoco ♩ = 148

2 Night Thoughts

2nds   G7C   3